SONG NOTEBOOK

The Smart Songwriting Journal for Guitar

This book is dedicated to all those who believe that words can change lives.

Published by **GuitarIQ.com**

Copyedited by Allister Thompson

Proofread by Dan Foster

Illustrated by Jasmin Zecchin

Contents

Online Bonus Material _ 5

Introduction _ 7

Things You Should Know _ 8

Using This Handbook _ 11

Songwriting Blocks _ 19

Tone Library _ 149

Additional Resources _ 158

Liked This Book? _ 159

Get Your Free Online Bonus Now!

This book comes complete with free online bonus material. We've compiled a companion website to enhance your reading experience. Extras include bonus downloads, and more!

Get your free bonus content at: **www.guitariq.com/sn-bonus**

Introduction

We've all been there…that dreaded feeling as you stare at the blank page. Waiting. Hoping for some seed of inspiration to spontaneously blossom into something amazing. The result is sometimes little more than a handful of chords and a few clichés. But it's a start, right? The good news is even though we can't cheat the songwriting process, we can certainly help it along! And while a good songwriting journal can't promise that next chart-topping smash, it can offer a better way of fostering creative ideas and capturing them when they happen.

So, what makes a *good* songwriting journal? And why use one at all? Well, admittedly, there's no single method of writing a song–no right or wrong. It happens differently for different people. If you've found something that works, go with it! That said, your smartphone, old notepad, or latest shopping list might be perfectly serviceable options, but that doesn't mean they're the most inspiring or effective choices.

This songwriting journal is purpose-built. It isn't a generic writing journal or basic notebook with the word *Songwriting* slapped on the front. While a pretty cover with a bunch of blank pages might look nice, it does little to help you write anything musical. In contrast, every section of this notebook was created with guitar players in mind, from space for lyrics and basic song information to dedicated sections for neck diagrams and guitar tab. There's even room for idea generation and blank templates for writing down your amp and effects settings.

The **Song Notebook** is for those who are done with compiling loose pages of lyrics and chord charts. It's for those who are tired of searching through random audio snippets of half-written songs. And for those whose music deserves more than to be scribbled on the nearest notepad, napkin, or coaster. Everything in this journal was created with a single purpose: to help guitar players write songs. And while no resource can promise to make you a *Billboard* chart-topping songwriter, this notebook will give you the basic tools to become a faster, better organized, and more productive one.

Things You Should Know

Feeling inspired? Well, don't let the following instructions keep you from writing that next masterpiece! However, if you can hold on for one minute, it's worth taking this introductory look at your new songwriting journal. To get the most out of this notebook, you'll need to understand the basic framework we'll be using. While most guitar players should find the layout of this journal fairly intuitive, below are some key points worth highlighting.

Writing Music

What comes first: music or lyrics? Without wanting to start that age-old *chicken* versus the *egg* debate, I'd suggest that most guitar players would consider themselves musicians before lyricists. As such, it's a safe bet that for many guitar players, music often comes first. After all, lyrics aren't poems; they're written to be sung, not read. This is by no means the *correct* order–there isn't one! It's simply the sequence that seemed most natural for this notebook.

When putting together this journal, it was important to provide space for writing down your musical ideas–not just your lyrical ones. As a general rule, you should always have some kind of recording device handy. However, this still doesn't capture the same detail as notating exactly what your fingers are doing.

What if I can't read music? (Let's face it, most guitar players probably can't.) No need to panic, this notebook has you covered! The space provided for writing down your riffs and progressions doesn't require you to read or write music. Instead, this journal uses neck diagrams and guitar tab. These methods are both simple to use and universally recognized by most guitar players. For those unfamiliar with these systems, however, they'll be detailed in the next section.

Writing Lyrics

With all those musical ideas blossoming in the back of your mind, let's talk about lyrics. This journal not only provides space for writing lyrics but also a sure-fire method for coming up with them in the first place. The lyrics section of this notebook revolves around a concept we'll call *Song Starters*. This principle is simple: Never start with a blank page. The blank page is the abyss where creativity goes to die! Or, at the very least, it's a good starting point if you're a fan of writer's block.

Song Starters are like your *pre-lyrics*. They represent the work you do before penning your final lyrical masterpiece. This process begins with brainstorming keywords based on the theme or story you have in mind. It then moves to refining and workshopping these keywords into short lyrical phrases. When done properly, the little nuggets of lyrical gold you uncover provide an excellent catalyst for building your final lyrics.

While this method is explained further in the next section, forming the building blocks of your song lyrics before you write them can be transformative. It can take a task that many guitar players find difficult and time-consuming and turn it into a process that's effective and even (dare I say it) enjoyable.

How It Works

This notebook is divided into 16 songwriting blocks. The idea is to provide you with enough space to write at least one new song a month for an entire year (with extra room for when inspiration strikes!). This notebook is for those who write music both casually and professionally. Regardless of whether you're working on your first few songs or your latest full-length album, here you'll find an effective method for capturing and organizing your ideas, both good and bad—the ones you'll want to show off, and the ones you'll want to throw out.

Your challenge (should you choose to accept it) is one new song a month for the next 12 months. Extra credit if you complete all 16 songwriting blocks by this time next year! Why one song per month? Even for the casual musician, this 12-song target is extremely achievable. You'll discover that a consistent writing habit (even one requiring minimal time commitment) will yield a growing repertoire of music in a relatively short time. Of course, this target isn't mandatory for using this notebook; however, it will help you get the most out of it.

In addition to music and lyrics, each songwriting block provides an opening section for outlining the core elements of your song. This includes details like the name, date, key, time, and tempo, along with space for summarizing the overall idea, theme, or situation you have in mind. As a bonus, at the back of this notebook you'll also find a section labeled the "Tone Library," which provides handy templates for noting amp and effects settings as you experiment with different sounds during the writing process.

Finally, for the best results, I recommend that you couple this journal with some kind of recording device. This needn't be fancy; most smartphones make great songwriting tools. It's helpful to label your recordings logically and then reference these file names in the appropriate sections of your journal. (Trust me, searching through a stack of random audio clips to find that one idea you liked isn't fun for anyone!) Remember, listening back to your ideas is a crucial part of refining them, just as writing them down is a crucial part of remembering them.

Using This Handbook

Now that we've outlined how to use this journal, let's take a more detailed look at each section of your song notebook.

Title: Song Details & Summary

The first section of your songwriting journal deals with the foundational elements of your song. This covers basic details like the title, date started, key signature, time signature, and tempo. However, it also includes room to overview the initial theme or story ideas you have in mind for your song. Here you can summarize feelings or experiences that crop up while writing. While they needn't be overly detailed or developed, these types of notes are especially handy when it comes to writing the lyrics for your tune. Below is a template of how this might look.

Example:

Song Title: MY NEW SONG

Date: 8 / 11 / 17

Key: E Major

Meter: 4 / 4

Tempo: 98 **BPM**

Notes:

- I'm writing this song while sitting at...

- To me, the vibe of the song feels...

- It makes me think of the time I...

- I want this song to be about...

- Maybe the chorus of this song might need...

- The bridge of this song feels like it should...

Music: Chords & Riffs

Under the sections titled "Guitar Chords" and "Guitar Riffs," you'll find space to notate your musical ideas. These blank templates function like the standard neck diagrams and tab you'll encounter in most sheet music for guitar. The good news is that you don't need to read music or have an in-depth understanding of music theory to write down what you're playing. This method provides a simple way to get your ideas down on the page quickly and easily.

If you're unfamiliar with these types of templates, the basic rule is: Just write down what your fingers are doing. With chord shapes, it's simply a matter of marking down the location of each finger on the fretboard. Even if you're not sure what a particular chord is called, you'll at least have a record of how it's played. This is especially helpful if you like experimenting with unique chord voicings or open tunings. Here's an example of what this looks like:

VERSE CHORDS

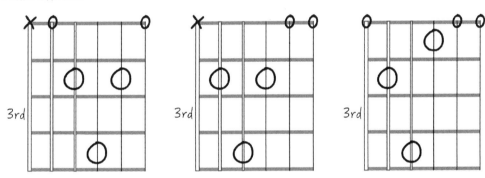

Likewise, we can use a similar method for notating guitar riffs or solo ideas. When using guitar tab, the bottom line represents the low E string and the top line represents the high E string. All you need to do is write down the frets you're playing in sequence. For those who understand a little about reading music, it's also beneficial to include some additional rhythmic notation. However, in its most basic form, tablature can be written as a simple stream of numbers, as pictured here:

INTRO GUITAR RIFF

Lyrics: Words, Phrases & Song Starters

Brainstorm & Refine

The first column in this section of your songwriting journal is titled "Brainstorm." Once you have a theme, situation, or story in mind for your song, the next step is to get those creative juices flowing. The goal is simple: Start dumping it all out of your head and onto the page. Write down whatever relevant words or short phrases come to mind. It doesn't need to be pretty, it doesn't need to be inspired, and, most of all, it doesn't need to be good. Don't overthink it! There's a big secret to finding your muse—it's called *getting started*.

Once you've filled this column with ideas, read back through your list and highlight the words or short phrases you like. This is your chance to weed out the clichés and focus on those terms that clearly represent the emotion or scene you're trying to portray. At this point, it may be helpful to use a dictionary or thesaurus to further develop your list of keywords.

The next column is titled "Refine." Use this space to workshop and expand upon your initial shortlist of keywords and phrases. Pay careful attention to the emotive weight behind certain terms. What does the imagery represent to you? What feelings does it evoke? How does this reflect the overall theme or message of your song? Examine your shortlist of words and experiment with tweaking them to more effectively illustrate what you're trying to say.

As an example, let's picture the scene of a young couple on a first date, sharing dinner by open firelight on the beach. (Super original, I know!) Here's a condensed version of how these columns might look.

Example:

Brainstorm	Refine
stars, ocean, _sunset_, sky, _tide_, waves, beach, sand, _lights_, distant traffic, music, _talking_, salt, _takeout_, _wine_, breeze, warmth, _fire_, first date, _dancing_, swimming, etc.	stars glowing bright, the hiding sun, high tide, sandcastles, city lights, talk for hours, cheap takeout, expensive wine, colored by firelight, dancing without music, etc.

Song Starters

The next section in your songwriting journal is titled "Song Starters." The goal here is to take your second list of workshopped words and expand them into phrases you can draw upon. Again, these lines needn't be perfect. They don't need to rhyme or fit into a particular structure—it's all about generating ideas. You don't have to use all these lyrics in your song—in fact, you don't have to use any of them! The purpose is to provide you with a creative springboard. Don't spend hours staring at a blank page waiting for creativity to strike and wondering why you don't feel inspired. Creativity is a muscle—exercise it and amazing things will happen!

Once you have a framework of solid ideas in place, you'll find that writing lyrics becomes quicker, easier, and more enjoyable. Let's look at an example of what some Song Starters might look like based on our previous list of keywords.

Example:

The stars dissolve into city lights

The sun goes to hide behind the horizon

High tide floods our houses made of sand

We've got cheap takeout and expensive wine

You wanna dance even when there's no music

We talked like we had nowhere else to be

Lyrics

The final part of each songwriting block in your songwriting journal is titled "Lyrics." If you follow the previous steps as outlined, by now there should be plenty of fuel for that lyrical fire. Pick up your guitar—it's time to finish writing your song! There are no rules here; your Song Starters are simply the kindling. What you do with them is up to you. Perhaps select a handful of your strongest ideas and structure each section of your song around them. Or compile entire sections of your song by rearranging your Song Starters to flow in context. Again, these ideas exist for inspiration only; they can be tweaked, changed, and even disregarded.

Here's an example of how you might create song lyrics using ideas generated by your Song Starters.

Example:

VERSE 1

The sun hides on the horizon line

As the stars dissolve into city lights

With cheap food and expensive wine

We dance barefoot in the rising tide

Ultimately, the final result always takes some workshopping and rewriting. (I suggest using a pencil!) However, it's likely that the more time you spend generating good ideas, the better the chance you'll end up with a good song. To this end, let's depart with one final nugget of wisdom for working with your lyrics. It's the golden rule of engaging writing: *Show, don't tell*! Always consider the picture your words create for the listener. What do your lyrics look, sound, smell, taste, and feel like in the context of your song's unique story?

For example, contrast the following lines:

"You broke my heart and tore it apart. Now I'm just so lonely."

"You took my dog and my favorite car. Now the house is so damn quiet."

These phrases convey a similar meaning. However, while the first line describes the general situation, it offers little depth or insight into the story. It *tells* what the writer is feeling but doesn't *show* what they're going through. The second line says the writer is heartbroken, without literally needing to spell it out. As a result, it carries more weight and meaning. It's less clichéd, more conversational, and far more engaging for the listener.

Tone: Amp & Effects Settings

The final section at the back of this journal is titled the "Tone Library." Any good stage tech will be familiar with this method for recalling amp settings quickly and easily. You simply mark in each circle where the dials on your amp are pointing, anywhere from zero to 10 (or 11, depending on how hard you rock!). This method also works well for rack effects and individual guitar pedals.

For guitar players, songwriting is often about experimenting with different *sounds*— not just progressions and riffs. Your Tone Library can function as a handy cheat sheet for noting down these new tones as you discover them. How you label these templates will depend on the gear you're using. However, here are two examples of how these could be laid out. (Obviously, the dials on each diagram would be set to taste.)

Examples:

Name: MY AWESOME AMP TONE

Volume	Drive	Treble	Middle	Bass	Master	Reverb	Presence
◯	◯	◯	◯	◯	◯	◯	◯

Name: MY KILLER DRIVE PEDAL

Gain	Treble	Bass	Level	–	–	–	–
◯	◯	◯	◯	◯	◯	◯	◯

Songwriting Blocks

Welcome to your songwriting blocks. If you've read the instructions closely, it's time to get started!

Song Title:

Date: _____ / _____ / _____

Key: _____

Meter: _____ / _____

Tempo: _____ BPM

Notes:

Guitar Chords

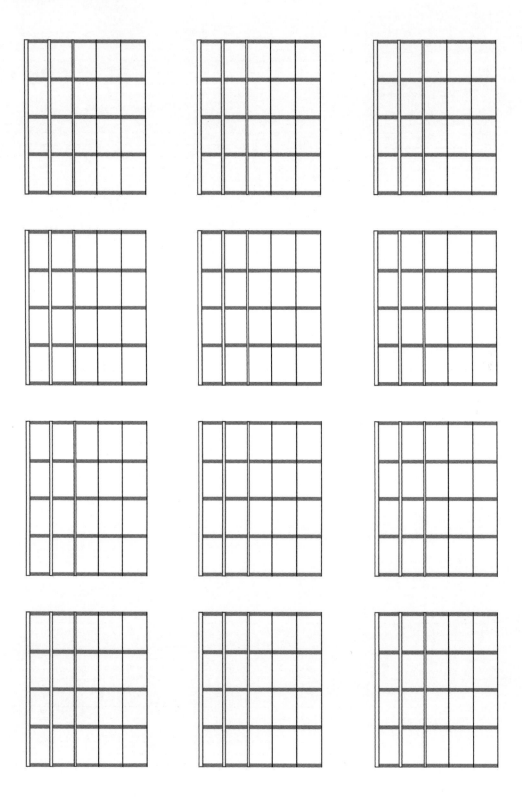

Guitar Riffs

T
A
B

T
A
B

T
A
B

T
A
B

T
A
B

T
A
B

T
A
B

T
A
B

Words & Phrases

Brainstorm	Refine

Song Starters

Lyrics

Song Title:

Date: _____ / _____ / _____

Key: _____

Meter: _____ / _____

Tempo: _____ BPM

Notes:

_____

_____

_____

_____

_____

_____

_____

_____

_____

_____

_____

_____

_____

_____

_____

_____

_____

_____

Guitar Chords

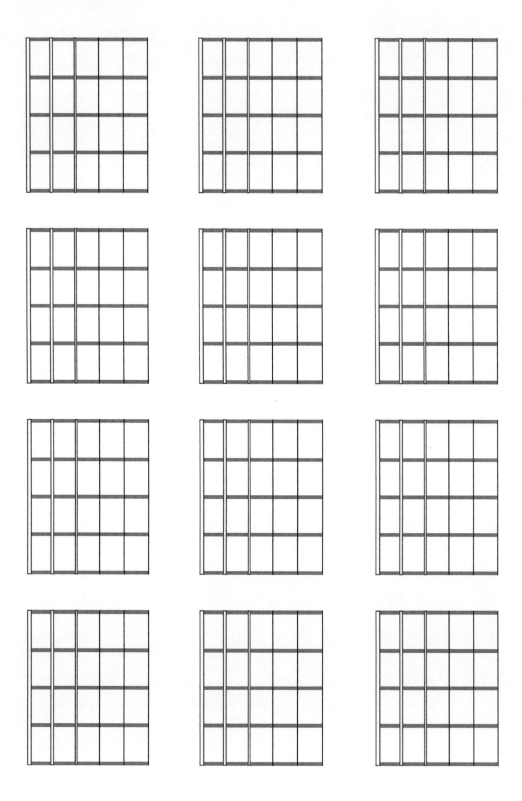

Guitar Riffs

Words & Phrases

Brainstorm	Refine

Song Starters

Lyrics

Song Title:

Date: _____ / _____ / _____

Key: _____

Meter: _____ / _____

Tempo: _____ BPM

Notes:

Guitar Chords

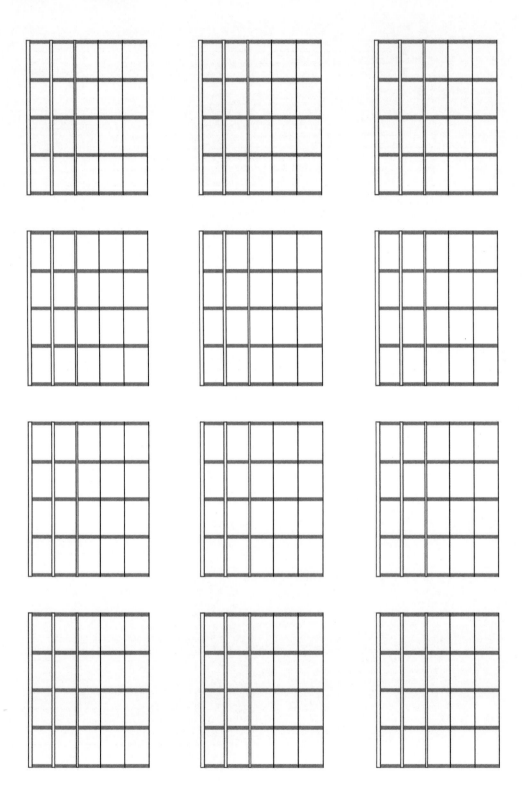

Guitar Riffs

```
T
A
B
```

```
T
A
B
```

```
T
A
B
```

```
T
A
B
```

```
T
A
B
```

```
T
A
B
```

```
T
A
B
```

```
T
A
B
```

Words & Phrases

Brainstorm	Refine

Song Starters

Lyrics

Song Title:

Date: _____ / _____ / _____

Key: _____

Meter: _____ / _____

Tempo: _____ BPM

Notes:

_____

_____

_____

_____

_____

_____

_____

_____

_____

_____

_____

_____

_____

_____

_____

_____

Guitar Chords

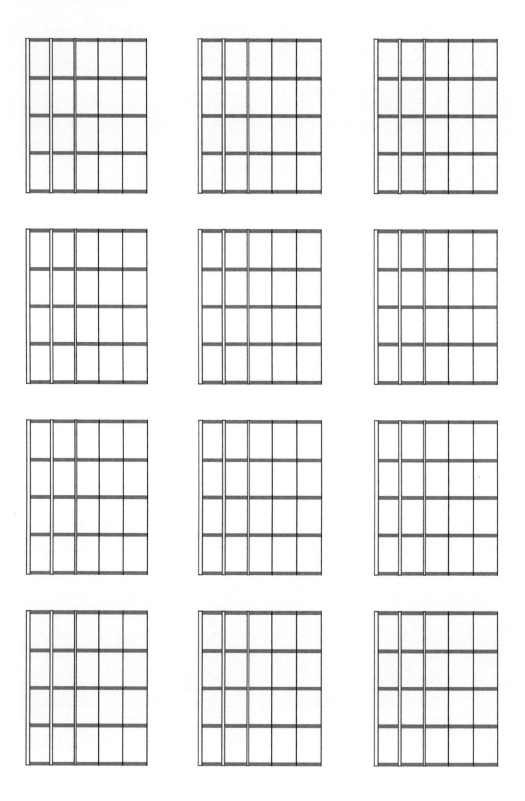

Guitar Riffs

```
T
A
B

T
A
B

T
A
B

T
A
B

T
A
B

T
A
B

T
A
B

T
A
B
```

Words & Phrases

Brainstorm	Refine

Song Starters

Lyrics

Song Title:

Date: _____ / _____ / _____

Key: _____

Meter: _____ / _____

Tempo: _____ BPM

Notes:

_____

_____

_____

_____

_____

_____

_____

_____

_____

_____

_____

_____

_____

_____

Guitar Chords

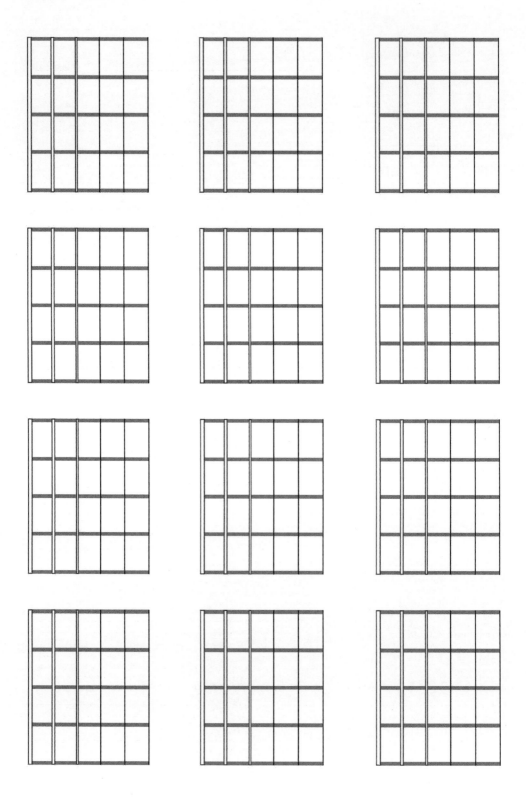

Guitar Riffs

```
T
A
B
```

```
T
A
B
```

```
T
A
B
```

```
T
A
B
```

```
T
A
B
```

```
T
A
B
```

```
T
A
B
```

```
T
A
B
```

Words & Phrases

Brainstorm	Refine

Song Starters

Lyrics

Song Title:

Date: ___ / ___ / ___

Key: _____

Meter: _____ / _____

Tempo: _____ BPM

Notes:

Guitar Chords

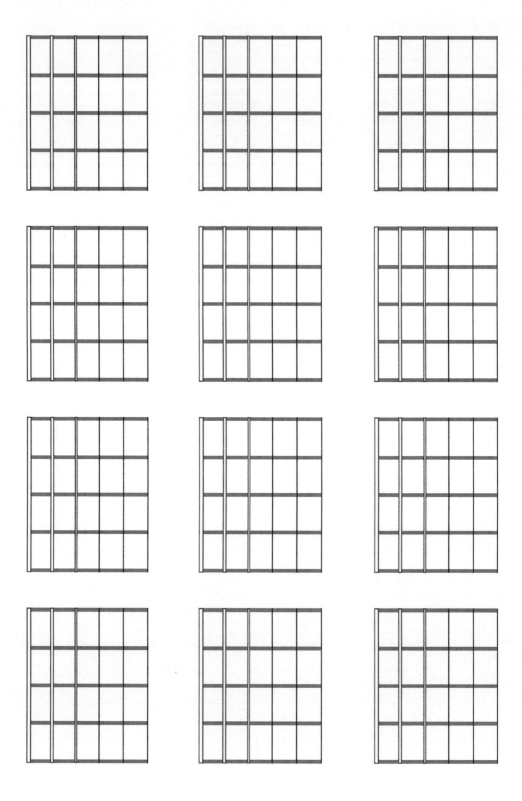

Guitar Riffs

```
T
A
B
```

```
T
A
B
```

```
T
A
B
```

```
T
A
B
```

```
T
A
B
```

```
T
A
B
```

```
T
A
B
```

```
T
A
B
```

Words & Phrases

Brainstorm	Refine

Song Starters

Lyrics

Song Title:

Date: _____ / _____ / _____

Key: _____

Meter: _____ / _____

Tempo: _____ BPM

Notes:

Guitar Chords

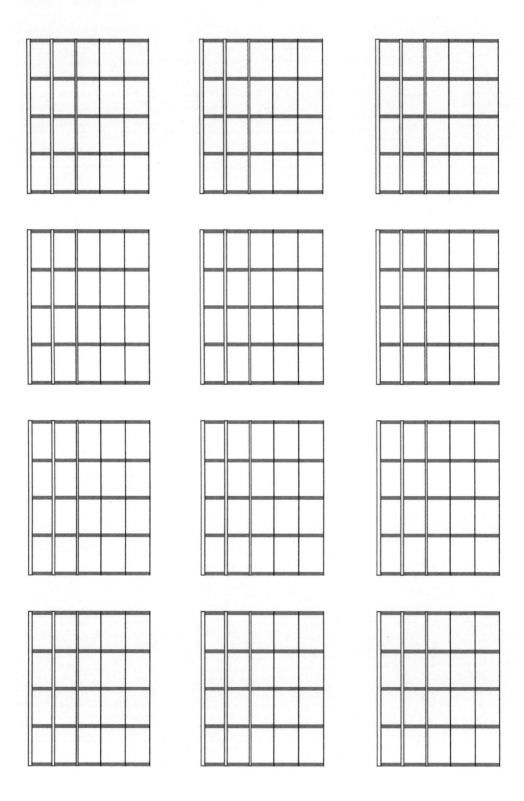

Guitar Riffs

Words & Phrases

Brainstorm	Refine

Song Starters

Lyrics

Song Title:

Date: _____/_____/_____

Key: _____

Meter: _____/_____

Tempo: _____ BPM

Notes:

Guitar Chords

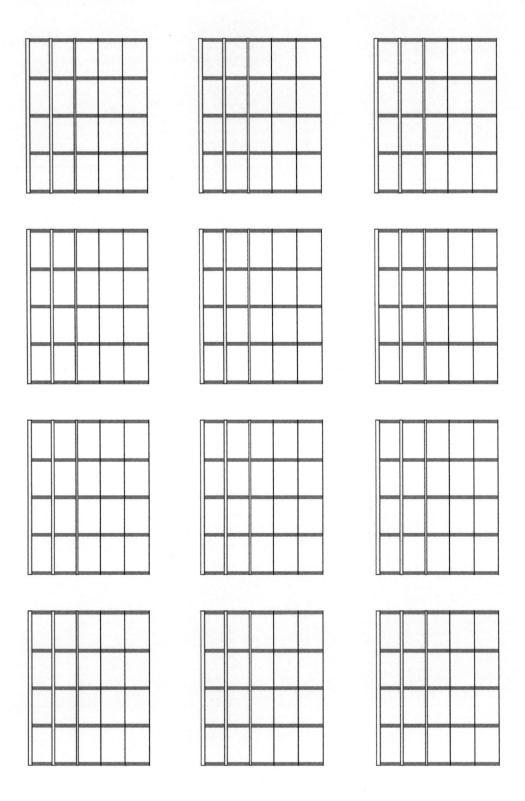

Guitar Riffs

```
T
A
B
```

```
T
A
B
```

```
T
A
B
```

```
T
A
B
```

```
T
A
B
```

```
T
A
B
```

```
T
A
B
```

```
T
A
B
```

Words & Phrases

Brainstorm	Refine

Song Starters

Lyrics

Song Title:

Date: _____ / _____ / _____

Key: _____

Meter: _____ / _____

Tempo: _____ BPM

Notes:

Guitar Chords

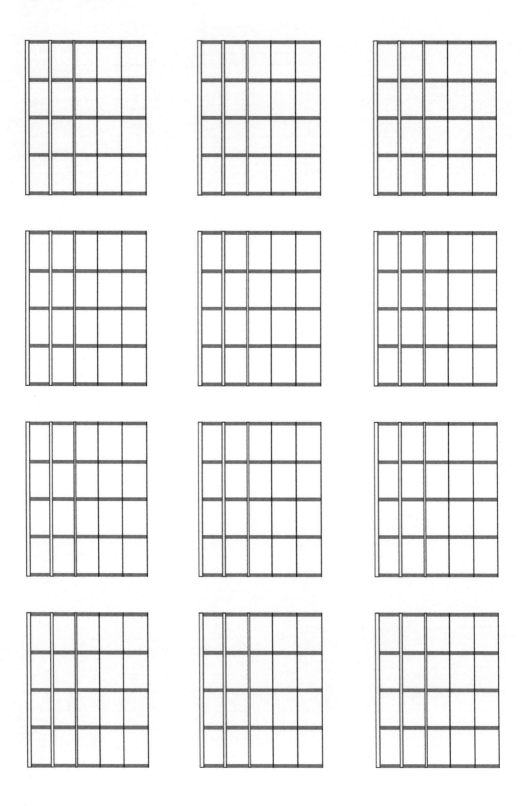

Guitar Riffs

```
T
A
B
```

```
T
A
B
```

```
T
A
B
```

```
T
A
B
```

```
T
A
B
```

```
T
A
B
```

```
T
A
B
```

```
T
A
B
```

Words & Phrases

Brainstorm	Refine

Song Starters

Lyrics

Song Title:

Date: ____ / ____ / ____

Key: _____

Meter: _____ / _____

Tempo: _____ BPM

Notes:

Guitar Chords

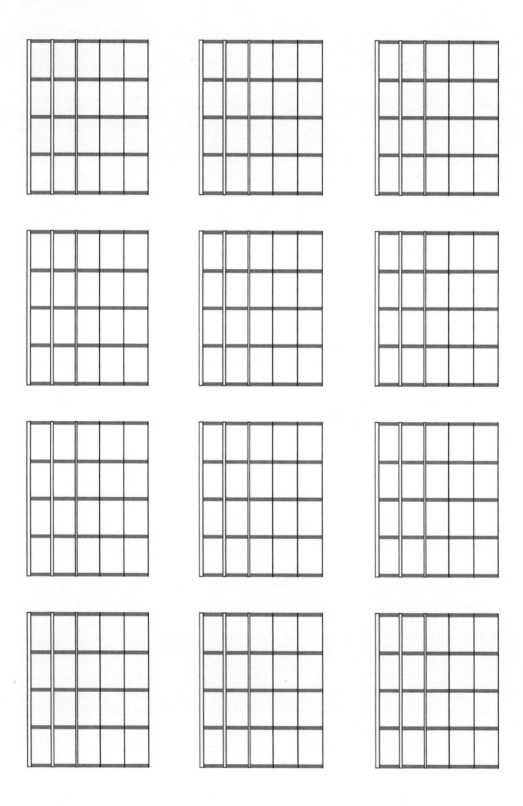

Guitar Riffs

Words & Phrases

Brainstorm	Refine

Song Starters

Lyrics

Song Title:

Date: ____ / ____ / ____

Key: _____

Meter: _____ / _____

Tempo: _____ BPM

Notes:

Guitar Chords

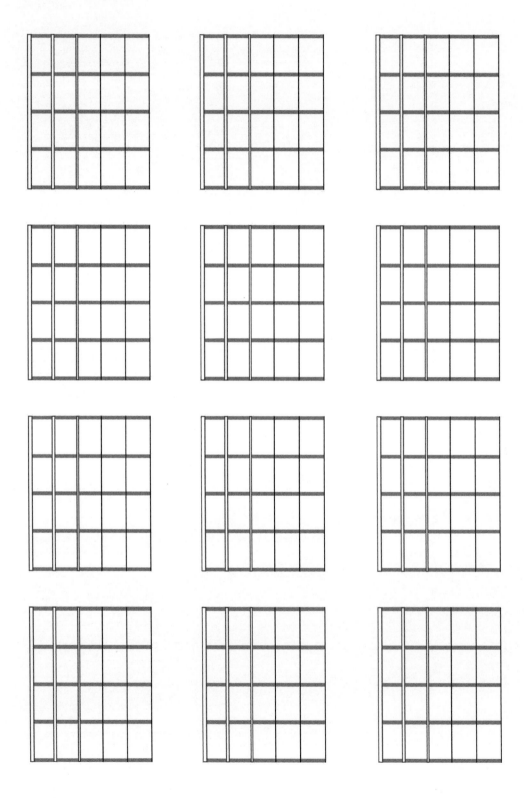

Guitar Riffs

Words & Phrases

Brainstorm	Refine

Song Starters

Lyrics

Song Title:

Date: _____ / _____ / _____

Key: _____

Meter: _____ / _____

Tempo: _____ BPM

Notes:

Guitar Chords

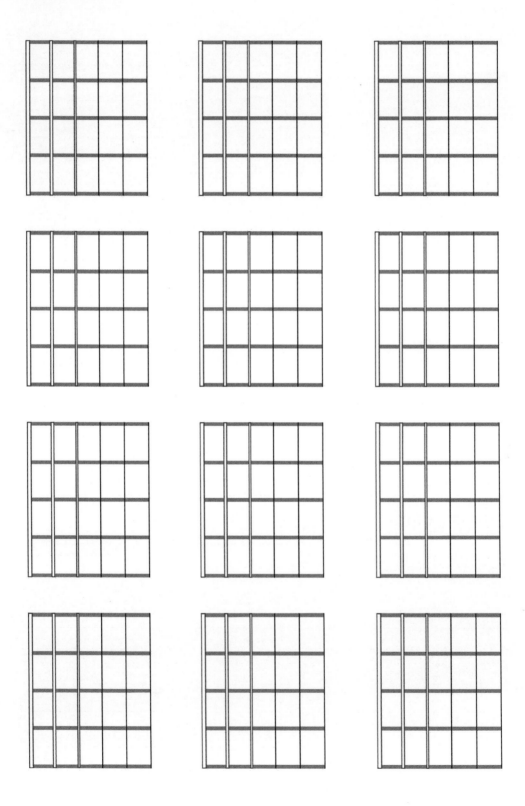

Guitar Riffs

```
T
A
B
```

```
T
A
B
```

```
T
A
B
```

```
T
A
B
```

```
T
A
B
```

```
T
A
B
```

```
T
A
B
```

```
T
A
B
```

Words & Phrases

Brainstorm	Refine

Song Starters

Lyrics

Song Title:

Date: ____ / ____ / ____

Key: _____

Meter: _____ / _____

Tempo: _____ BPM

Notes:

Guitar Chords

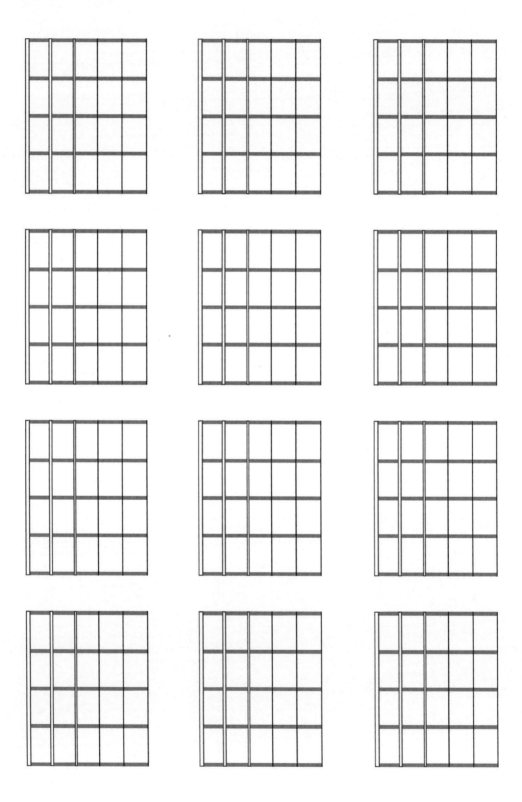

Guitar Riffs

Words & Phrases

Brainstorm	Refine

Song Starters

Lyrics

Song Title:

Date: _____ / _____ / _____

Key: _____

Meter: _____ / _____

Tempo: _____ BPM

Notes:

Guitar Chords

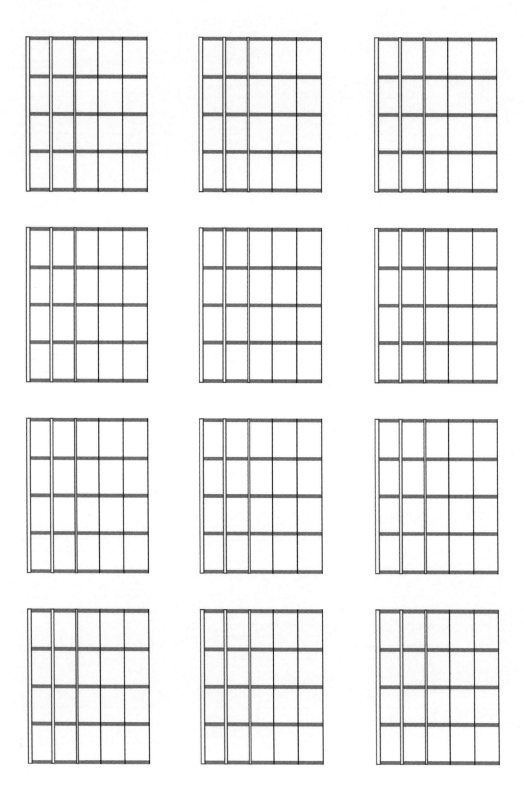

Guitar Riffs

Words & Phrases

Brainstorm	Refine

Song Starters

Lyrics

Song Title:

Date: _____ / _____ / _____

Key: _____

Meter: _____ / _____

Tempo: _____ BPM

Notes:

Guitar Chords

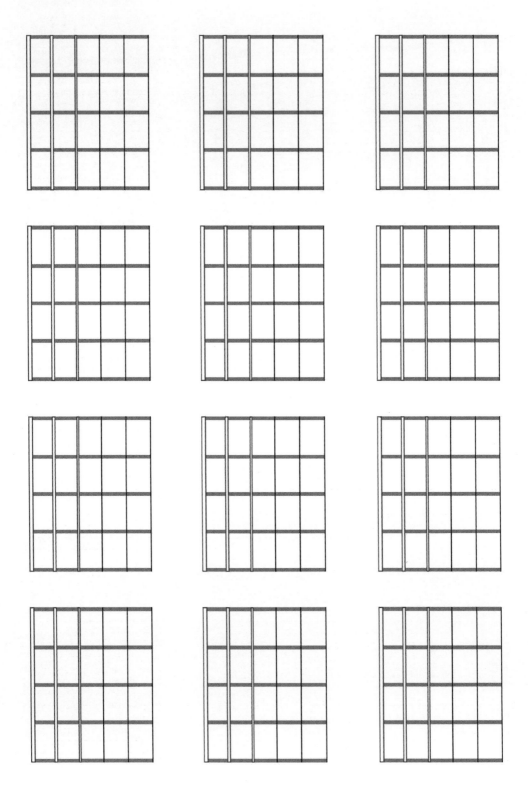

Guitar Riffs

Words & Phrases

Brainstorm	Refine

Song Starters

Lyrics

Song Title:

Date: _____ / _____ / _____

Key: _____

Meter: _____ / _____

Tempo: _____ BPM

Notes:

Guitar Chords

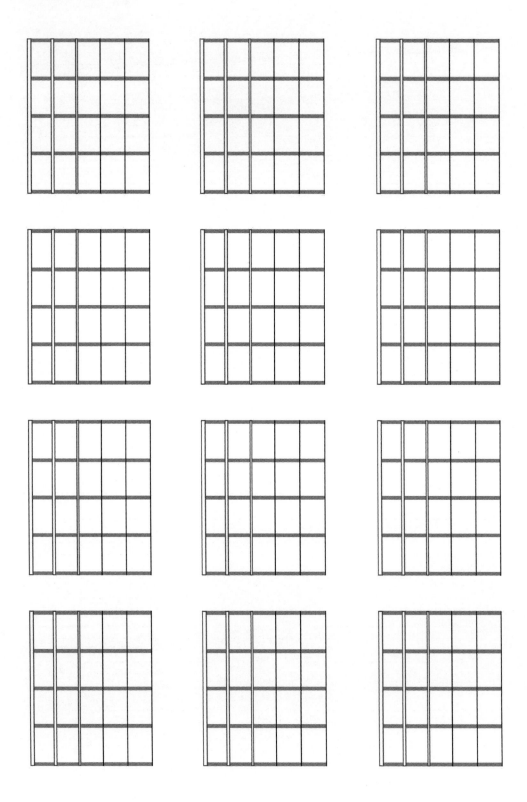

Guitar Riffs

Words & Phrases

Brainstorm	Refine

Song Starters

Lyrics

Tone Library

This is your Tone Library! When you need inspiration, here's a reminder of those killer sounds you've discovered this year.

Amp Settings

Name:

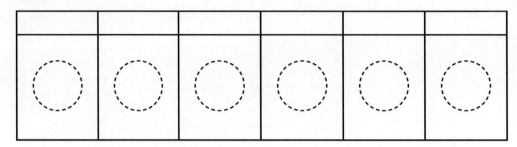

Name:

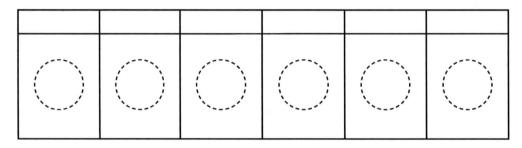

Name:

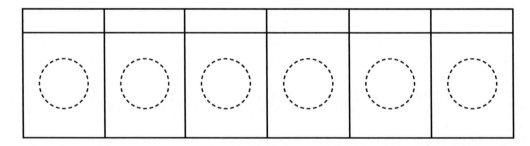

Name:

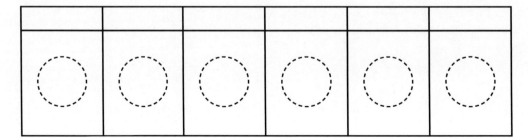

Name:

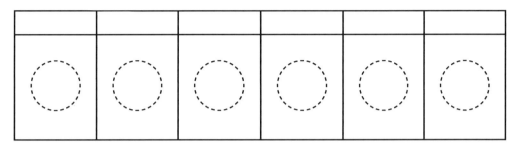

Name:

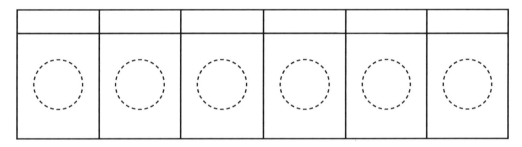

Name:

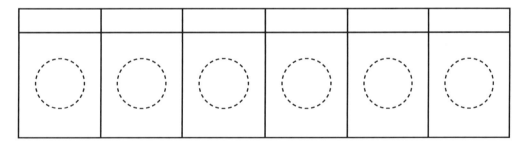

Name:

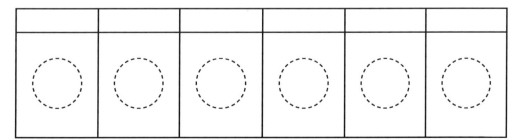

Name:

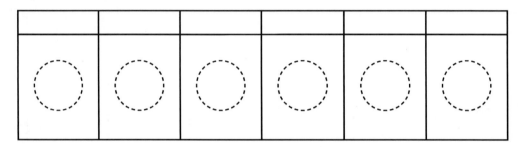

Name:

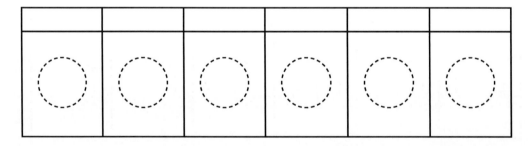

Name:

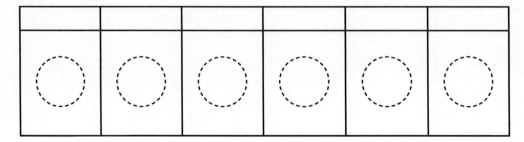

Name:

Name:

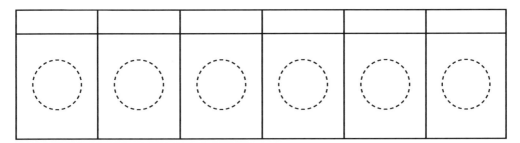

Name:

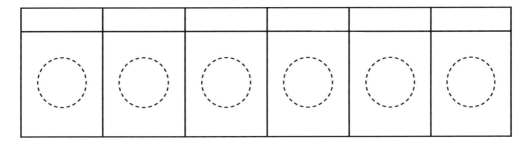

Name:

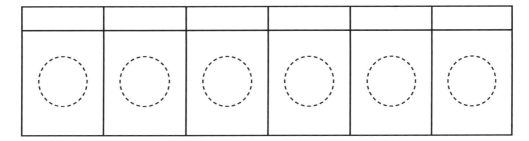

Name:

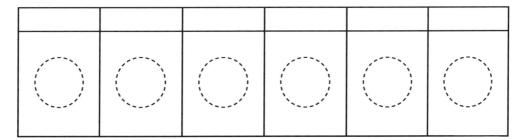

Effects Settings

Name:

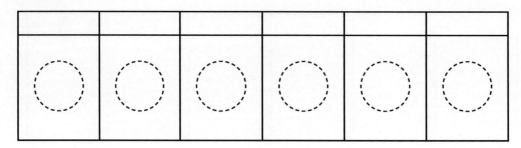

Name:

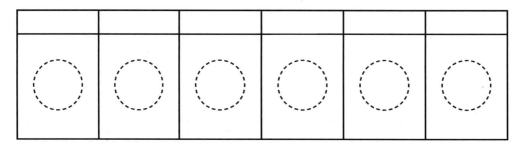

Name:

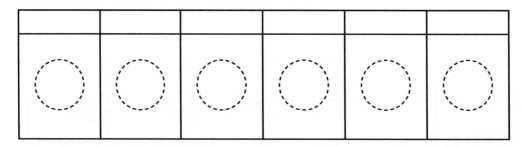

Name:

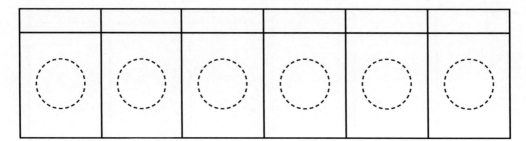

Name:

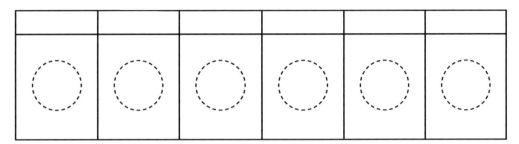

Name:

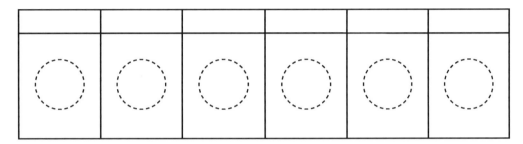

Name:

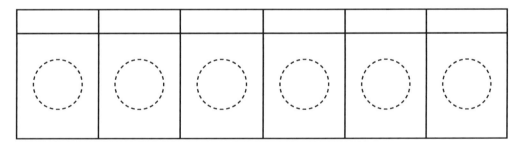

Name:

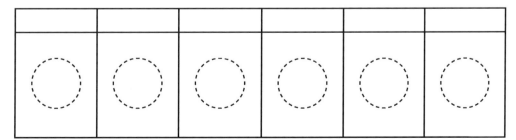

Name:

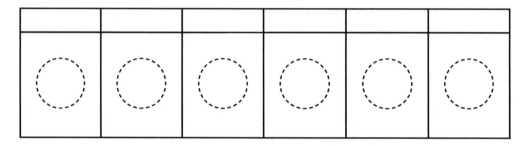

Name:

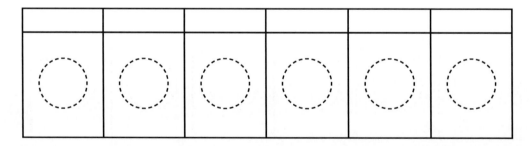

Name:

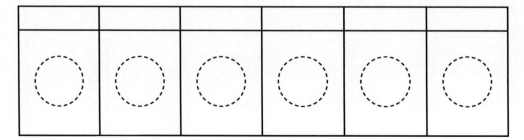

Name:

Name:

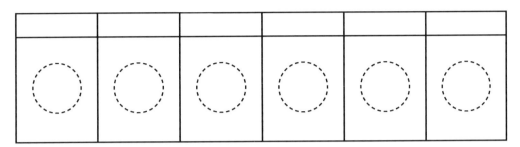

Name:

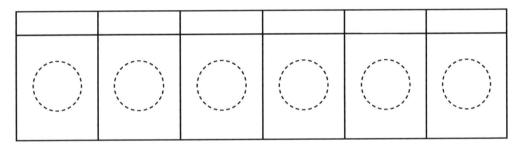

Name:

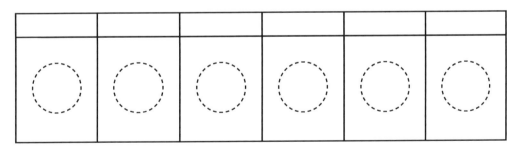

Name:

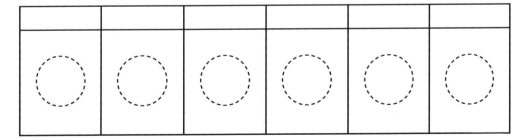

Additional Resources

For more resources, including great free content, be sure to visit us at:

www.guitariq.com

Stay in touch with all the latest news. To connect with us online, head to:

www.guitariq.com/connect

Would you like to read more? For a complete list of our books, check out:

www.guitariq.com/books

Remember to grab your free online bonus! Get the bonus content for this book at:

www.guitariq.com/sn-bonus

Interested in a master class with us? To check out our online workshops, go to:

www.guitariq.com/academy

Liked This Book?

Did you find this notebook useful? You can make a big difference in helping us spread the word!

While it would be nice to have the promotional muscle of a major publishing house, independent authors rely heavily on the loyalty of their audience. Online reviews are one of the most powerful tools we have for getting attention and finding new readers.

If you found this book helpful, please consider helping us by leaving a review at your place of purchase. Reviews needn't be long or in-depth; a star rating with a short comment is perfect. If you could take a minute to leave your feedback, it would be sincerely appreciated!

Printed by Amazon Italia Logistica S.r.l.
Torrazza Piemonte (TO), Italy